Kids for Kids

Messages of Hope & Love from the Nation's Children

Edited by
Leslee Ann Michaels

Happy Heart Press

Lake Fairlee, Vermont

Thank You

A very special thanks to the children and teachers around the country who made Kids for Kids a reality, to Debra Howe for her invaluable help and support and to Linda Aldrich for making the manuscript so beautiful.

Copyright © 1997 Leslee Ann Michaels

Cover Design by Lightbourne Images
Cover Illustration by Becca Beisler, Grade 5

Published by Happy Heart Press
A Division of Happy Heart Cards Inc.
Lake Fairlee, Vermont 05045
800/603-9024   802/333-4667 (Fax)

Library of Congress Cataloging-in-Publication Data

Michaels, Leslee Ann, Editor
Kids for Kids: Messages of Hope & Love from the Nation's Children

p. cm.
ISBN 1-890059-68-4

1) Oklahoma City Federal Building Bombing—Juvenile literature.
2) Children—United States—Correspondence.
3) Children—Psychology.   I. Title.

HV6432.K54 1997   976.6'38   96–080051

Printed in Hong Kong

First Edition

10 9 8 7 6 5 4 3 2 1

Bookstore Distribution:
Login Publishers Consortium (LPC Group)

Gift Store Distribution:
Sourcebooks

Foreword

Though Kids for Kids was inspired by the bombing in Oklahoma City, there is a universality in the children's messages of eternal hope. With innocence, simplicity and wisdom they speak about trusting the reverence of life, in spite of it all.

They remind us that you can always count on the sun rising each morning and winter turning into spring. You can count on the wonder and beauty of nature, the life of green, the grace of blue. You can count on light to diminish the darkness. You can count on love to overcome hate.

The Kids for Kids project was only one small trickle in a sea of love that came pouring into Oklahoma City. There were countless individuals who selflessly gave of themselves in whatever way they could to help people in need. So much of the human family came together united as one with compassion, kindness and empathy.

There were people who risked their own lives to save others. Leaving with us an example of courage never to be forgotten. In the face of a terrible tragedy, love was the lesson we learned. The overwhelming concern from individuals worldwide was a lasting testament that there is more goodness than evil in the world and that love is infinitely stronger than hate.

With all our hearts, the children and I pray for peace to come to our world. We desire goodness and blessing, kindness and compassion, life and love. Our wish is that hatred is banished forever from the human heart so that we can live together in love and peace.

It is our hope that you find comfort and healing in the poems, letters and art in our book. The nation's children are reaching out in love to you.

Leslee Ann Michaels

Our Gift of Healing

This poem is dedicated to all the families who lost their loved ones.

Remembrance

In the rising of the sun, and in the dawning of each day
I will remember you.
In the opening of buds, and the rebirth of Spring
I will remember you.
In the blueness of the sky and in the warmth of Summer
I will remember you.
In the rustling of the leaves and in the beauty of Autumn
I will remember you.
In the blowing wind and in the peace of Winter
I will remember you.

So long as I live, you shall live
for you are a part of me, as I remember you.

LAM

April 19, 1995

Do not turn your back; you cannot run away.
Our problems will be there tomorrow
if we don't solve them today.
Do not close your eyes; don't turn that dial.
Nothing goes away if you do not face it,
if you turn away in denial.
This world that we live in isn't always a safe place,
Not always a pink curtain trimmed with ruffles and lace.
Beyond the draperies that we imagine,
lies a dark and sorrowful sight,
So we keep the curtains closed
pretending everything's all right.
How quick are we to jump and point a finger at the innocent.
For it was "one of us", a stone cold heart
and a mind twisted and bent.
He who is so cruel and doesn't stop to think;
and he who would kill someone in cold blood and not even blink.
He speaks with tongue and treads on the same green earth,
And yet he felt the need to hurt you,
and the country of his birth.
He was angry at the system and chose violence to be heard,
But now he is hated; no one will listen, not to one useless word.
Those who are dead, cannot be brought back,
but they live on in memory,
Just as April 19, 1995, will surely go down in history.

Erin Rounds
Grade 6

Dear Kids

Molly Bowman, Grade 5

Compassion. Sara Lornitzo, Age 16

To The Kids

You need to have hope,
There will always be praying for you,
Someone who looks over you and all of us every day,
That very special person is God,
He watches over all of us.
He comforts us when we need comforting.
He prays for us when we need prayers.
And most important of all,
He gives us love when we need it the most.
And that is what you need to think about now.

Jamie K. Lawrence
Age 11

♡ ♡ ♡ ♡ ♡ ♡ ♡ ♡ ♡ ♡ ♡ ♡ ♡

I Care

Spring, then summer
unlatch the magic that runs free
Memories of flowers and grass
Memories of butterflies and frogs.
Early flowers make me happy
Remember there are still people around
the world that care for you.

Caringly,
Kendell Lensing
Age 10

Sunflower. Aaron Langlois, Grade 3

Dear Kids,

I know your hearts must be breaking,
but I'm sure that happiness will
come again to your city.
I'm glad you have each other
to help heal your broken hearts.
My thoughts and prayers will always be with you.

Eliza Keller
Age 9

♡ ♡ ♡ ♡ ♡ ♡ ♡ ♡ ♡ ♡ ♡ ♡ ♡

Everything is there for You

The sun is always shining for you.
The flowers are always blooming for you.
The air will always be there to cool you off.
Your friends and family members are thinking about you.
The love and hope that everyone has will help
you live your life peacefully.

I wrote this letter to tell you
how much I care and love.

Brodie Ladue
Age 10

Have a Balloon. Tabitha Klam, Age 5

Dear Kids,

Our school planted a rosebush for you.
We will think of you every spring
as the roses bloom.

Nicole Fisher
Age 10

Love Doves.
Jody McCoy, Age 11

Dear Kids,

Pansies are my favorite flower.
I love their funny little faces.
Just thinking about them makes me smile.
I'm going to plant a garden of pansies for you.

Lindsey Rizzo
Age 9

Friends. Jessica Disnard, Grade 2

With all our Love

I think of your sadness,
I know how you feel.
And with all of our love,
we will help you all heal.

Christopher Hitchcock
Age 10

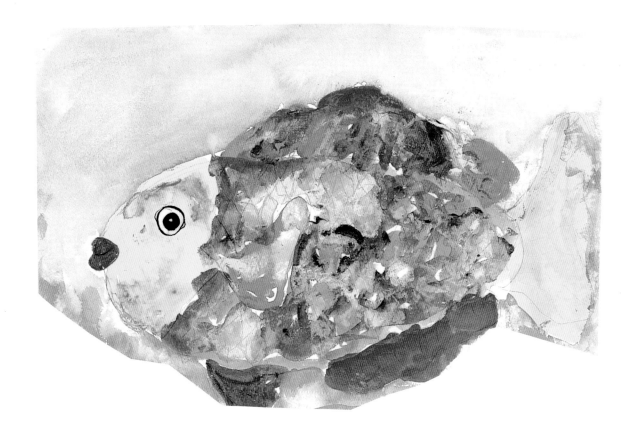

Parrot Fish. Brieanna Weinstein, Age 11

Lady Love. Danielle Young, Age 7

Love

Starry Night. Tyler Beaulou, Grade 6

Love

I believe in love.
Love brings people together.
Hate tears them apart.

Just look
where hate takes us.
To war
To killing
To more hate.

Let's not hate.
Let us love.

Lydia Quackenbush
Age 10

♡ ♡ ♡ ♡ ♡ ♡ ♡ ♡ ♡ ♡ ♡ ♡ ♡

Peace and Love

peace and love,
That's how the world should be
with peace and love.
I wish everybody could see
the beauty of this world,
the way I'd like it to be.

Damon McGinn
Age 11

Heartwings. Rachael Blanchfield, Age 12

Love is Special

Love is something special
It's floating in the air
so once it floats by you,
you know what to do.
Tuck it way down in your heart
and hope it's there to stay
and when something sad happens
don't let love float away.

Julian Merrill
Age 9

Cuddling. Courtney Riel, Grade 8

15

Love is in the Air. Josh Taft, Grade 6

Love and Peace

I wish this world could
be a peaceful place.
With love spread all
over the place.

Kristen Aloisio
Age 11

Caring and Goodness

Caring and Goodness
enough to fill
the world and us.

Matthew Boyar
Age 8

The Cure

I wish people would stop hurting each other.
There must be a cure for hatred.
I believe the cure is love.

Blake Premer
Grade 4

Love Heals

Love is the best thing in the world.
It is strong and powerful.
Love heals broken hearts
and makes us whole again.

Juan Carlos Acosta
Age 10

World of Love. Lizzy Rodriguez, Age 11

Faith

Turtle. Chloe Powell, Grade 5

Messenger to Heaven

Good-bye balloon in the sky
you've made me happy
to see you set free
bring my prayers to heaven

to thank God
for the love in my heart
thank God
for the people who care
thank God
for the people who help
thank God
for the people who share
thank God
for the people who heal
thank God
for the people who hope
thank God
for the people who are brave
thank God
for the people who cope

You've made me happy
to see you set free
Good-bye balloon in the sky.

Eden Alessi
Age 9

God

It helps me to have faith in God.
When bad things happen, I feel really sad.
But I believe there's more good than bad in the world.
My belief in God helps me.

Brian Nasajon
Age 10

Believe

As the windmills turn
And the ravens cry,
A star of hope is hanging out there
In the midnight sky.

Believe.

Karin S. Amer
Age 12

Dreams. Patrick Miller, Age 14

Blanket of Love

Peace, love, compassion and hope.
Sing and pray
God will hear our prayers.
He will answer with His love and
He will send it down like a blanket over us.

Kashner Montague Worthington
Age 11

Make Me a Dream

Mr. Sandman come and make
me a dream filled with love.
Make my mind fly free as a
white morning dove.
Make my dream full of fears
rush away in a river of tears.
Make me a dream where
tranquillity flows,
like the soft summer wind blows.

Kristen Williams
Age 13

Green Leaf. Edge Cole, Grade 6

Hope

Swan. Hoyt Henderson, Age 8

Singing Meadow

There is a ray of hope shining through every window,
Go on and take a look, across the singing meadow,
where birds do whistle overhead,
Flowers springing in their bed,
A stream that sparkles bright and clear,
The tinkling melody of rocks and rushing water is so pleasant
and so very dear,
Eagles glide across the wide terrain,
Cloudless sunshine appears again,
The sun does smile very brightly,
Autumn breezes pass through so lightly,
Morning dew makes sweet music as it drops,
Glittering rain does fall and sprinkles atop the crops,
Golden corn and wheat do spring,
Farmers hearts begin to ring,
Winter comes and snow has an icy twinkle,
These memories will never wrinkle,
I reach out to the world and say,
There is a ray of hope shining through every window,
Big or small, or wide or tall.
Tattered ones and shattered ones,
There is a ray of hope, shining through every window,
Go on and take a look across the singing meadow.

Megha Mahajan
Age 12

Hope

Such a peaceful word,
Hope.
A reason to keep on living
when the world is dark.
Hope.
Knows the dawn is coming
and the darkness will end.
Hope.

Josefina Massa
Age 13

Sunrise. Erica Faughnan, Age 12

Butterfly and Rainbow.
Jenna Ware and Jimmy Calver, Grade 4

Isn't That Enough?

I wish I could hug the world,
Squeeze out all of the fear
Then fill it with love;
I wish I could wipe away the tears,
All the little children's tears
and put smiles,
Big bright smiles
On their shining cheeks,
I wish I could push faith and joy
Into every afraid and lonely heart,
But all I can do is pray,
Isn't that enough?

Heather Rounds
Age 11

Peace

Hurt no living thing.
Bird nor butterfly with fragile wing.
Let us have no hatred in our hearts.
But be joyful and sing.

Molly McCumber
Grade 4

Flowers. Ashley Bergeron, Age 10

Rain

The rain falls,
the world goes gray,
happiness and love seems washed away.

The goodness seems gone,
we assume it won't return,
we think to cry and not to learn.

But remember . . .
the rain came for a reason,
it makes the flower strong,
listen to the bird and his now sweeter song.

The rain often falls hard,
and it fills us with sorrow,
but did you ever think you'll be stronger
tomorrow?

Elizabeth Wyzik
Grade 5

♡ ♡ ♡ ♡ ♡ ♡ ♡ ♡ ♡ ♡ ♡ ♡ ♡

Rainbow

Hope is the rainbow,
that comes after the rain.

Marie Schiffer
Age 12

In Flight. Ashly Dubreuil, Age 8

Songbirds

Hope is
the songbirds who sing
when the storm is through
they make me think
that we can sing too.

Brett Stogel
Age 10

Purple Crocuses

Hope is the flower
that blooms through the snow
pretty purple crocuses
are the ones I know.
This little flower
is a lovely thing
It tells me of the coming spring.

Taylor Moore
Age 10

Budding Tree. Joshua Thurston, Age 11

Comfort

God saw a tear,
and kissed it away
with the smile of a friend.

Wai-Han Chan, Age 11

I Wish

I wish I could hug you and hold you
and wipe away your tears.
Words don't seem like enough.

Erica Kelley
Age 12

Clown. Adam Staizkiewicz, Age 5

Love Lives Forever

Some people are so separated from each other
that they can never be joined together again.
Sometimes I remember my grandpa
who died when I was four,
but still I remember him in my heart and
I feel his greetings in the morning from heaven.
I look into the sky when I feel sad
and I see his greetings. Sometimes to cheer me up
I see animals of clouds and I smile to thank him.
So remember if somebody died in your family
don't cry when you remember the memories
just remember that they are always with you.
Love lives forever in the heart.

Lynn Fayad
Age 9

Heavenly Light

When I look up at the evening sky
I like to think I see
all the people I've loved and lost
smiling down at me.

Jenna Katz
Age 13

Cry

I always feel better after
I've had a good cry.

Jonathan Walker, Age 10

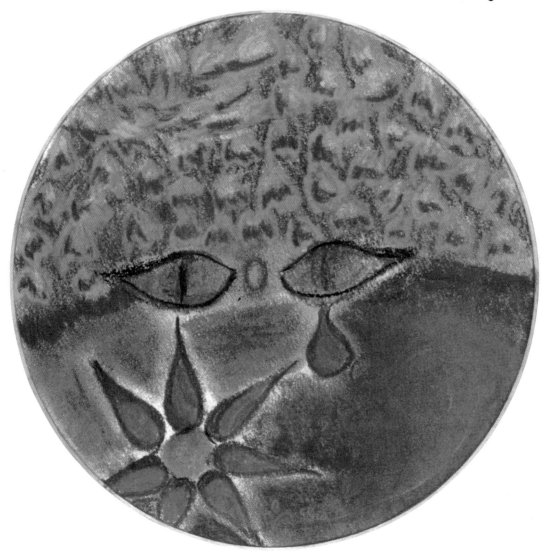

Tears. Sarah Burke, Age 14

Dove

I heard the dove call out my name and sing a song of praise.
Of peace and hope and harmony of those who have raised.
The song of hope went to my heart and dried away my tears.
So I could remember the loved ones
I've lost throughout the years.
I heard the dove call out my name and sing a song of praise.
Of peace and hope and harmony
as his song faded gently away.
He will take his song to others to tell what I now know.
And slip away as gently as drifting flakes of snow.

Alicia Cooper
Age 10

♡ ♡ ♡ ♡ ♡ ♡ ♡ ♡ ♡ ♡ ♡ ♡ ♡

Remember

Remember their laughter,
the touch of their skin.
The beauty of their face,
the glory of their grin.

JUST REMEMBER!

Diana Smirnov
Grade 3

Thomas Placey, Grade 4

Think Good Thoughts

There is a song up in the air;
it is love.
There is a song to sing;
it is happiness.
There is a song to come;
it is peace.
Now think of a happy place,
hold that thought . . .

Alle Weil, Age 11

Reach Out

Don't ever feel you are alone.
There is always somebody there to reach out to.

Chase Goodstein
Age 11

Horse in a Field. Rachael Little, Age 9

Nature's Healing

Dolphins. Shelsey Weinstein, Age 8

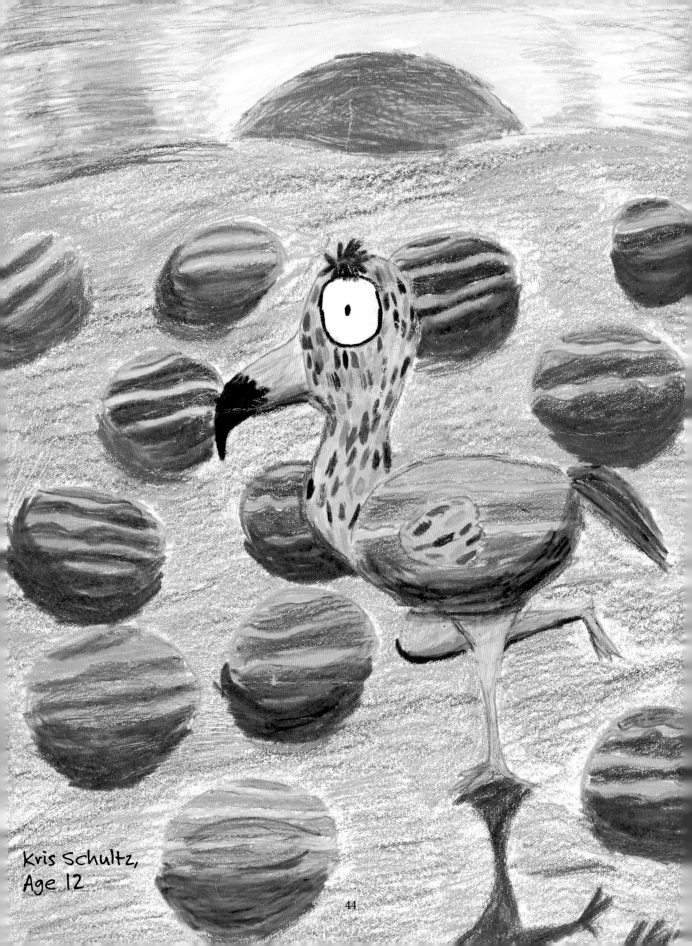

Kris Schultz,
Age 12

44

Nature's Healing

Rolling oceans topped with white lace,
Surround the people, the human race.
Thundering storms are good, not bad,
For they birth the flowers which make people glad.

Whispering trees hold the wonders of the Earth,
Which create the singing rivers, and fill them with mirth.
As they role through the canyons, the birds learn their song
Who enchant the people with their cries all day long.

With this people are lifted from their burden of hate,
The birds arrived not a minute too late.
Hopes for the future have come at last!
Now all the hatred is in the past.

Joy Harrison
Age 12

Violet

Violet is an evening sunset,
The color of the sky I love most.
Violet is a sweet feeling
That blocks away the anger.

Parker Shorey
Grade 3

Carnival. Catherine McNally, Age 8

The Rain Cloud of Hope

The rolling wind,
The buzzing bees,
The flying black birds,
And you and me.

The rain cloud of hope,
The joys of life,
The tears of heaven,
A world without strife.

The sound of snow,
The patterns of lace,
The taste of the cold,
A smile on every face.

The wish you made,
The hope won't part,
The glasses of wisdom,
A love in your heart.

The rolling wind,
The buzzing bees,
The flying black birds,
And you and me.

Miriam Gluck
Age 12

Apple Picking Time. Jeanette Horvath, Age 8

Unity

Playground. Tiffany Wirkkata, Age 8

Hands. Kyle Mullin, Grade 6

We Are the Children

We are the eyes for a world that is blind.
It is groping in the darkness for a peace it cannot find.
We are the ears for a world that does not hear.
The sound is straining to break through
but is blocked by hate and fear.
We are the voice for a world that will not be heard.
We try to speak, but will you listen to our word?
We are the children; the promise of tomorrow.
Lift up your voices and drown out the sorrow.
We have one song yet many voices.
Still we have one world and many choices.
We have one life and only one chance.
If we are not careful, our Earth will be gone at a glance.
We have one hope and a greater dream.
So let us put our differences aside and form a team.

Samantha Quinon
Age 12

Family

Everyone I see
is a sister and brother to me.
We should not hurt one another
we are one big family.

Christina Laurin
Age 13

Together As One. E. Alessi, Age 10

Poem of Caring

I am a hopeful person, I care
I don't discriminate people,
Because of what they wear.
I wish the Earth to be happy,
And I simply cannot bear
To see hate, racism, violence,
In my town, and everywhere
So let us get up and
Show that we love,
Stop and do not swear,
We are hopeful people,
And we DO CARE!

Jonathan Bowley, Age 11

♡ ♡ ♡ ♡ ♡ ♡ ♡ ♡ ♡ ♡ ♡ ♡ ♡

United We Stand

We can all make the world
a better place.
If we think positive and
have a little faith.
When people destroy it,
We will rebuild it.
When people pollute it,
We will clean it.
And when people have fear
We will be there.
It's our choice to do the right thing
Have some faith and hopefully we will.

Jennifer Efron, Age 11

Tree of Life. J. Egna, Age 10

Never Again . . .
PLEASE!

People went through so much pain
I'm hoping and praying
it will never happen again.

"Please, God make the hate stop"
Oh, I'm sorry. I was just saying a prayer
I truly wish hate would go away
right through thin air.

The act of evil was bad enough
Now, how are we going to stop it
that's tough.

Maybe we could pull together
not make one tear
all as one
with love and no fear!

Glenn Todaro
Grade 4

♡ ♡ ♡ ♡ ♡ ♡ ♡ ♡ ♡ ♡ ♡ ♡ ♡

A Nation in Mourning

We need a world of peace, unity and love.
And we need to have faith in the one above
But we must take a moment
And remember those innocent that died
And then erase the tears stains
from a nation that mourned, a nation that cried

Heather Hawkes
Grade 8

A Word of Thanks

Thank you for supporting us in our efforts. All proceeds from sales will accrue to the Oklahoma City Schools' Kids for Kids Fund. This fund helps children deal with the trauma of the bombing by supplementing counseling costs and supporting arts education programs. Dr. Guy Sconzo, Assistant Superintendent of Public Schools, chairs the Kids for Kids' Citizens' Advisory Committee which reviews requests from teachers, parents and children for support of specific programs.

Included for your interest are copies of "Tears on My Pillow" which I shared with kids in classrooms throughout the country to inspire them and "A Mission of Love" which summarizes the passion and purpose of Kids for Kids.

The children's overwhelming faith and trust reinforced and strengthened my own belief in the goodness of life; that right ultimately triumphs over wrong, good over evil and love over hate.

Leslee Ann Michaels

Tears On My Pillow

Oh what a tragedy
happened in Oklahoma City.
The whole word cries
wiping the tears from their eyes.
Watching the death toll rise
of so many innocent lives,
so many innocent lives.

And who is to blame
for causing such sorrow and pain.
Oh what a shame, what a shame!

What tears me apart
what really breaks my heart
is the defenseless people in there
and all the innocent babies and children in child-care
And to think this could happen anywhere.

Terrorism has come to America.

This kind of heinous crime
sadly happens all the time
in other places around the world.
Innocent men, women, and children
going to heaven's gate
because of horrible acts of hate.

What can we do for our sorrow?
How can we make a safer tomorrow?
How can we make this hatred cease,
so we can be a world living in peace?

LAM

A Mission of Love

The children and I
pray for a world
where love reigns supreme.
Peace, friendship, and harmony
is our dream.

The wish in our heart
is that hatred would forever part.
No more hurting of one another.
All people are my sister and brother.
As light has the power
to make darkness disappear,
the children and I pray
that love overcomes hatred and fear.

We want a world
where love reigns supreme.
Peace, friendship, and harmony
is our dream.

LAM